Pip, Lop, Mip, Bop and the Stuck Star

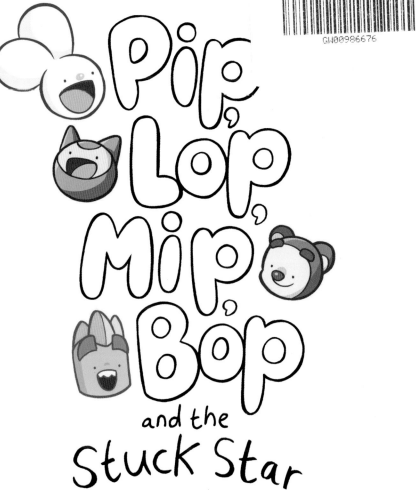

Written and illustrated by

Jamie Smart

OXFORD
UNIVERSITY PRESS

OXFORD
UNIVERSITY PRESS

Great Clarendon Street, Oxford, OX2 6DP, United Kingdom

Oxford University Press is a department of the University
of Oxford. It furthers the University's objective of excellence
in research, scholarship, and education by publishing
worldwide. Oxford is a registered trade mark of Oxford
University Press in the UK and in certain other countries

Text and illustrations © Fumboo Limited 2017
Inside cover notes written by Teresa Heapy

British Library Cataloguing in Publication Data
Data available

ISBN: 978-0-19-841509-1

10 9 8 7 6 5 4 3 2 1

Paper used in the production of this book is a natural, recyclable product
made from wood grown in sustainable forests. The manufacturing process
conforms to the environmental regulations of the country of origin.

Printed in China by Golden Cup

Acknowledgements

Series Editor: Nikki Gamble

At the bottom of the garden,
you might see a tiny cloud.

Pip, Lop, Mip and Bop are in the cloud!

Pip is clever.

Lop has long arms.

Mip is sleepy.

Bop is strong.

Pip, Lop, Mip and Bop are looking for things to do.

What shall we do?

Thinking!

All the stars look down to see.

WE will get you back up into the sky!

Star Power!

Pull!

Pull!